Top Hat

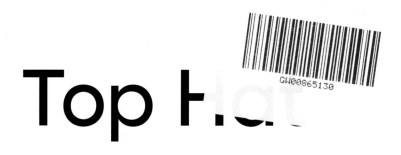

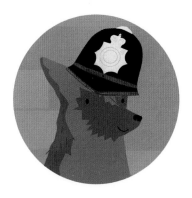

Kasia Reay

Illustrated by Alex Hoskins

Schofield&Sims

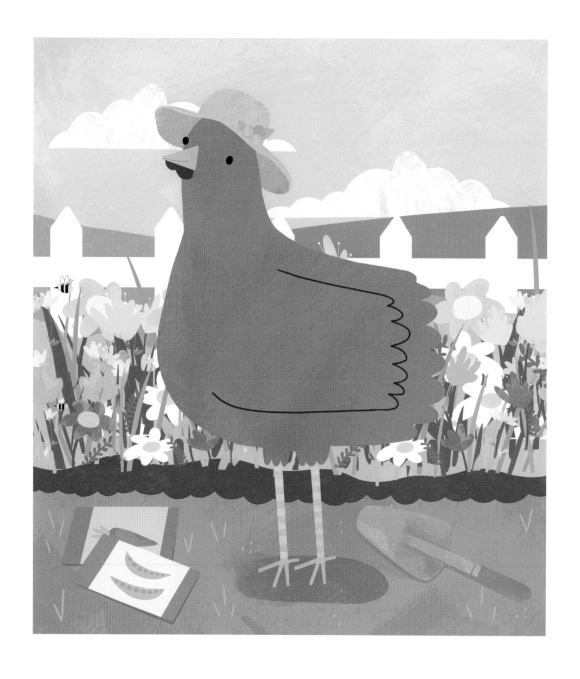

The hen has a hat.

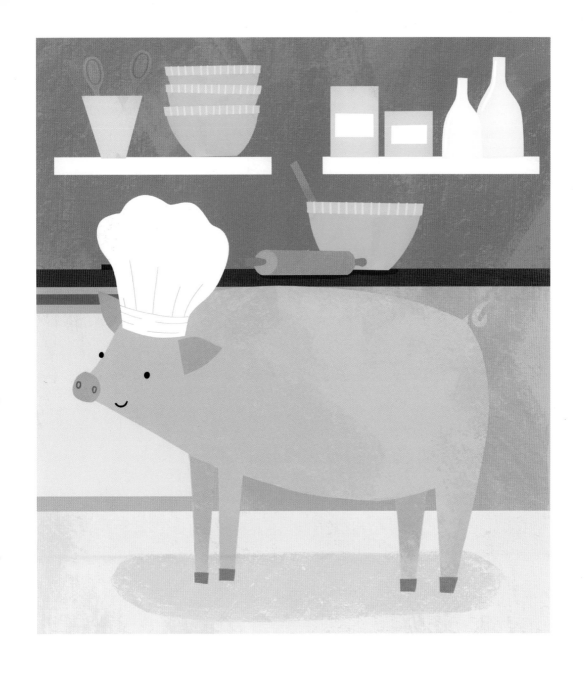

The pig has a hat.

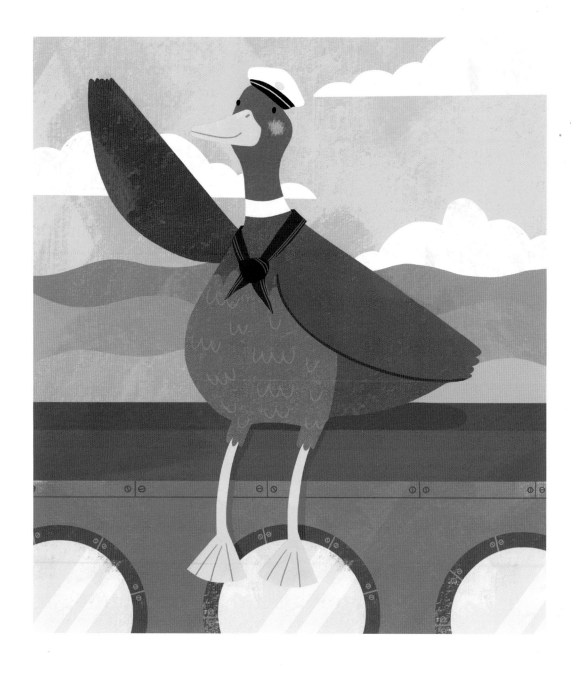

The du<u>ck</u> has a hat.

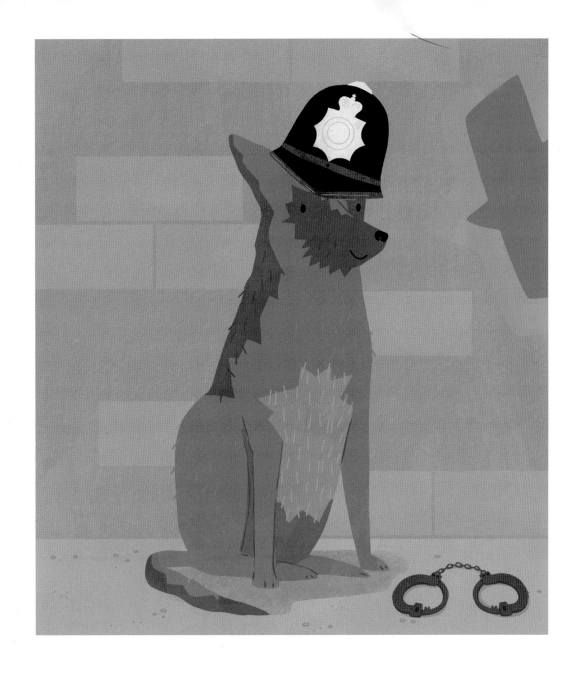

The dog has a hat.

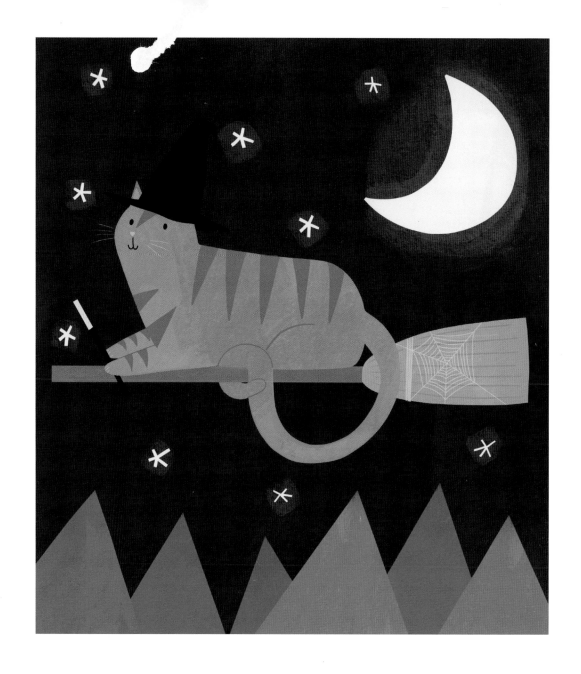

The cat has a hat.

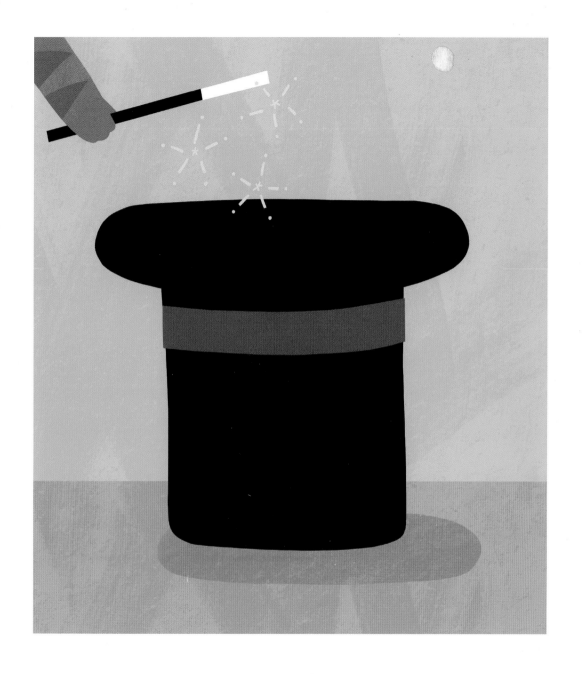

Tap, tap, tap...

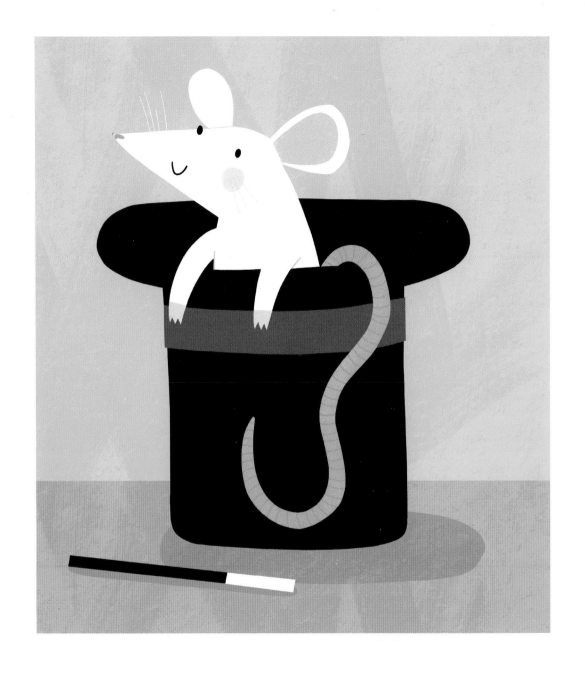

the top hat has a rat!